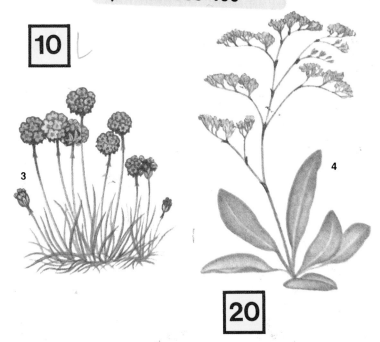

3 **Thrift**
You can find this on cliffs and rocks. The plant is like a
dark green cushion with flowering stems 10–20cm tall
growing up from it. The flowers appear in summer.

4 **Sea lavender**
Can cover large areas on sand-dunes or by muddy
seashores. The flowers are often dried for decoration.
They can last many weeks after picking.

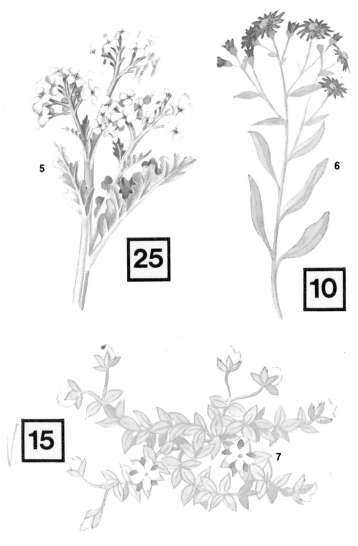

5

25

6

10

15

7

20

8

5 Sea kale

The leaves of this plant can be eaten as a vegetable.
Look for it on sandy beaches and where there are
chalk cliffs.

6 Sea aster

Common on cliffs and rocks or by muddy seashores. It
can grow as high as 1m.

7 Sea sandwort

You can find this plant on dunes and other sandy
places. The stem and leaves are fleshy and spread
over the ground.

8 Sea rocket

Search for this right by the sea. It grows out of sand
or shingle on the beach. Flowers appear from June to
August. Did yours have flowers?

9 Turnstone

The name of this bird tells you how it feeds. It finds small animals under stones and seaweed. You are most likely to find one on a rocky shore.

10 Oystercatcher

Look for one wading along the water's edge searching for its food of shellfish. Its beak is the perfect shape for opening shells.

11 Guillemot

In summer, these birds gather together in breeding colonies. They crowd on to narrow ledges on high cliffs. They only lay one egg, and do not build nests.

12 Puffin

Puffins nest in rabbit burrows or dig holes themselves on cliff tops. They also only lay one egg. Look out for their colourful striped beaks.

10

11

12

13 **Herring gull**
Watch for these birds standing in pairs. Most herring gulls keep the same partner for life, but they part during the winter.

14 **Black-headed gull**
This seabird has a red beak and legs. In summer its whole head is chocolate-brown. In winter it only has a brown mark behind each eye. At what time of year did you see yours?

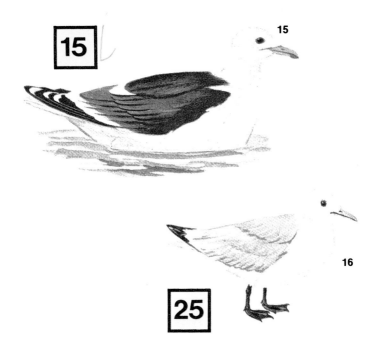

15 **Great black-backed gull**
The largest gull, this has a jet black back and pale pink legs. It is very fierce. Other birds keep well away from it! Listen for its call. You will know it by its very deep hoarse notes.

16 **Kittiwake**
Try to find this bird on cliffs in spring and summer. In winter it lives far out at sea. Listen for the call of 'kitti-wake', and note down when you hear it.

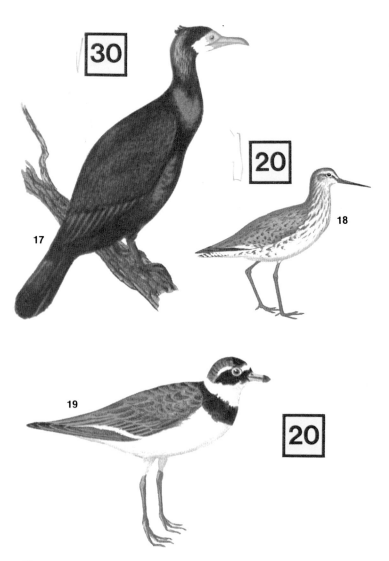

30

20

17

18

19

20

10

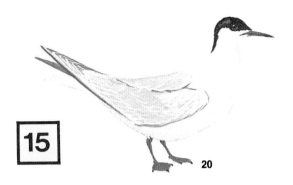

15

20

17 **Cormorant**
This is a glossy black bird. You may see it dive into the sea to catch fish. Do not confuse it with a shag – look for white on its thighs and its face.

18 **Redshank**
Search for one in estuaries and on muddy seashores. It uses its beak to reach for worms under the sand. It is called a redshank because of its red legs.

19 **Ringed plover**
You can find this bird on sandy or stony beaches. Look for it running along then stopping to snatch up food with its beak.

20 **Common tern**
This bird has a forked tail. Spot the black tip to its red beak and its red legs. You may see groups on sandy or muddy shores.

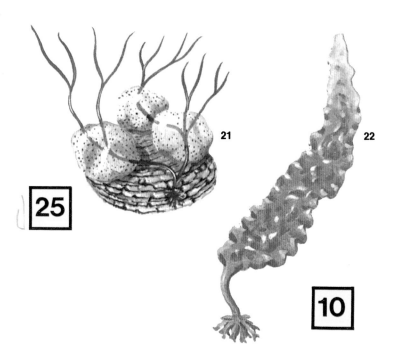

21 **Oyster thief**
A small seaweed which can be found attached to other seaweeds or shells. It is hollow and often floats on the surface of the water.

22 **Sea belt**
This grows up to 3m long, and you can use it to forecast the weather. Hang some up outside; it goes crisp if it is going to be dry, and goes soft and rubbery if it is going to rain.

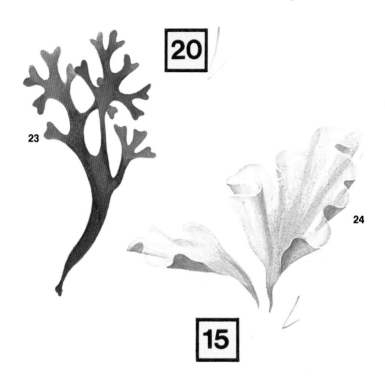

23 **Irish moss**
Look in rock pools for this purple seaweed. It glows underwater, but loses its beauty out of water. Move it to and fro in the water so that it catches the light.

24 **Sea lettuce**
You will find this in rock pools attached to small stones. It is very thin, and if you stretch it flat between your hands, you can see right through it.

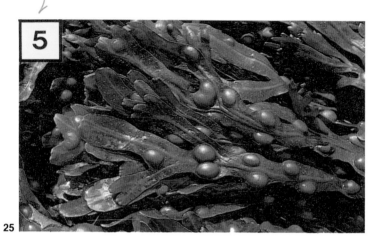

25

25 **Bladder wrack**
Grows on rocks, and has air bladders to help it keep upright in the water. If you squeeze one you will hear it pop. The bladders are usually in groups of 2 or 3.

26 **Knotted wrack**
Grows in large masses. Floats on the water, hiding the rocks below. Sometimes another seaweed, tandy, grows on it – can you find that too?

27 **Oarweed**
Found in shallow water attached to rocks. It can grow more than a metre long. How long was yours?

28 **Sea oak**
This looks as if it is covered with small pea pods. These are really air bladders to keep it upright. It grows on rocks.

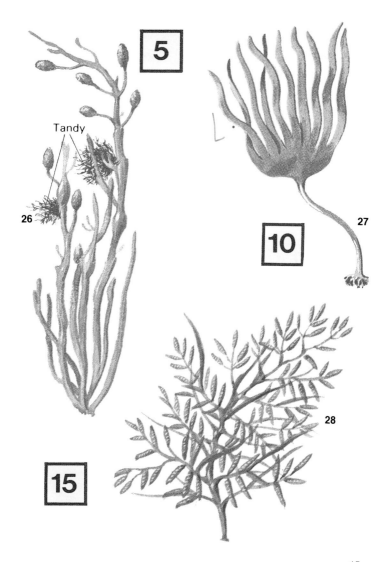

5

Tandy

26

27

10

28

15

15

This would be a very exciting find. Grey seals gather for breeding on rocky coasts, but you may see one stranded on the beach.

The young are called pups and are born with a white coat, but later they grow a harsh grey coat mottled with black. Their feet are flippers, so they can swim much better than they can move about on land.

Score 50 if you see a seal.

15

10

31

30

32

10

5

33

30 **Common cockle**
This lives on sandy shores. Look near the sea at low tide for a live one, but you may just find its shell. The rings on the shell are formed each year as it grows. If you count them, you will know how old it is.

31 **Acorn barnacle**
Look in and around rock pools for one of these. A barnacle lives for as long as five years. You will probably see lots all together.

32 **Flat periwinkle**
Feeds and shelters among seaweed. You may see a red, brown, black, yellow or white one. What colour was yours?

33 **Limpet**
Clings tightly to the sides of rock pools. When the tide is in it crawls about, always returning to the same place when the tide goes out.

34

20

34 **Razor shell**
It is difficult to find a living razor shell. They live under the sand, and can burrow half a metre down in three seconds! Look for empty shells on a sandy beach.

35 **Common mussel**
These creatures attach themselves by special threads to rocks and piers. There are often lots of mussels together. They are roughly oval, with one end more pointed than the other, and 1–10cm long.

36 **Great scallop**
There are several kinds of scallops. Look for one on sand or gravel in the water at low tide, or a shell that has been washed up. You may find both halves of its shell or just one half.

37 **Common whelk**
This large sea snail, about 8cm high lives in muddy sand or gravel. Empty shells are often covered with sponges and anemones. Did you find a live whelk or an empty shell?

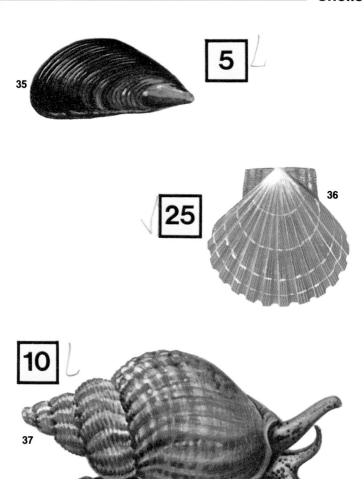

35

5

√ 25

36

10

37

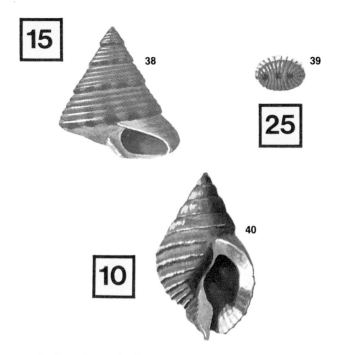

38 **Painted topshell**

Easy to recognize by its straight sides and pointed spire. It can be yellow or pink with red streaks. Search under ledges and behind seaweed for one. Where did you find your painted topshell?

39 **Cowrie**

This can be found on the underside of ledges at low tide. It is only about 1cm long, purplish-brown above and pale below. Score as well if you find an empty shell.

40 **Dog whelk**

Look on rocky shores for this creature. Live ones are often among barnacles and mussels which are its food. It grows up to 4cm high, and its thick, coiled shell can be white, brown or white and brown. What colour was yours?

41 **Common oyster**

You can find oysters attached to a rock or stone in shallow water. Oysters are cultivated as they are good to eat, and some make pearls in their shells. Did you find an oyster living naturally? Score too if you just find an oyster's rough shell.

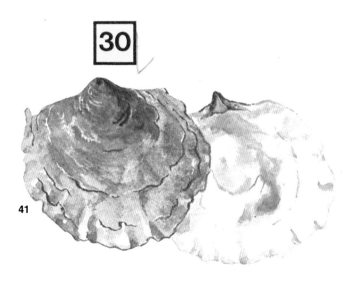

30

41

42

42 **Green shore crab**
An easy crab to spot! You can find one anywhere on the beach. It lives among seaweed, in rock pools or beneath rocks, and can grow up to 4cm long.

43 **Porcelain crab**
Look for one clinging to the underside of a rock. It is quite small, only about 1cm long, but has large nipper claws, and a rather hairy body.

44 **Hermit crab**
The hermit crab has no shell of its own. It lives in the empty shell of another creature. What sort of shell was yours living in?

45 **Edible crab**
These can be found under wide rock ledges. They are very strong, and you will find it difficult to get one out. They can grow up to 14cm long.

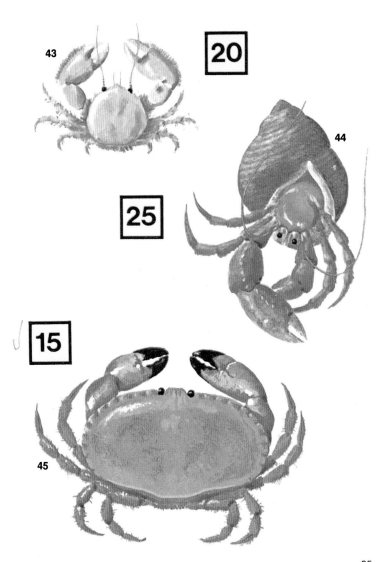

43

20

44

25

15

45

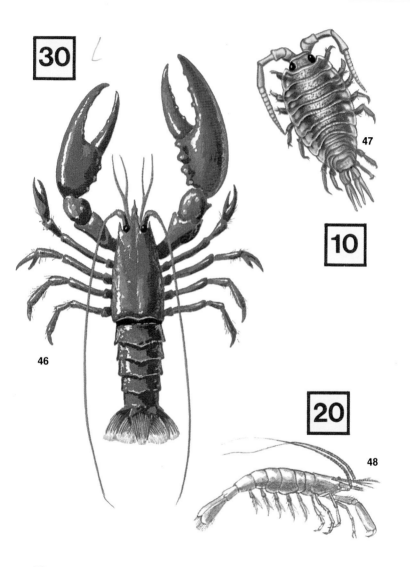

30

47

10

46

20

48

5 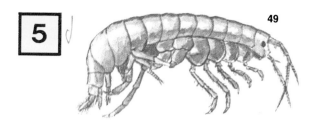 49

46 **Lobster**

These live among rocks, in cracks and holes and in caves. They are not common on the shore, but you may see one caught in a lobster pot. They can be up to 45cm long.

47 **Sea slater**

Only about 25mm long. Look for one in cracks and under rocks and seaweed high up on shore. They come out after dark.

48 **Shrimp**

You must look very carefully in sandy pools to find a shrimp. During the day it stays still, covered by a layer of sand. It can bury itself in about 20 seconds, by pushing the sand aside with its legs.

49 **Sandhopper**

These are found on beaches under stones or rotting seaweed on the strandline. They can jump up to 30cm but are only 2cm long!

50

20

20 **51**

52

25

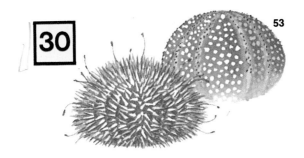

50 **Beadlet anemone**
You can find anemones in rock pools. Out of water, they draw in their tentacles, and then look like blobs of jelly stuck to the rock.

51 **Common starfish**
Most starfish have five arms which they can regrow if damaged or lost. The common starfish lives on rocky shores. It can cling on to the rocks.

52 **Purse sponge**
Sponges are animals. Look for them under rocky ledges at low tide level. You can also find this sponge attached to seaweed.

53 **Sea urchin**
Sea urchins have bodies covered with spines. They live on rocks and among seaweeds. You may find a shell (called a test). They are very delicate.

Interesting finds

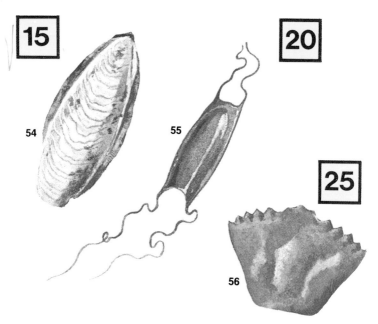

15

20

25

54

55

56

54 Cuttlebone

This is the internal shell of a cuttlefish. All birds like
the soft chalky bit, so it is sold for feeding to caged
birds. Watch for birds on the beach pecking at one.

55 Mermaid's purse

This is the egg case of a dogfish. A similar egg case
with a stiff point at each corner belongs to a skate or
ray. What sort of mermaid's purse was yours?

56 Crab's back

All crabs grow by moulting. As they grow, their shells
split. The crabs crawl out and grow another hard